# PLANTS vs. ZOMBIES™

## BULLY FOR YOU

Written by **PAUL TOBIN**
Art by **RON CHAN**
Colors by **MATTHEW J. RAINWATER**
Letters by **STEVE DUTRO**
Cover by **RON CHAN**

# PLANTS VS. ZOMBIES™

## BULLY FOR YOU

DARK HORSE BOOKS

President and Publisher **MIKE RICHARDSON**
Editor **PHILIP R. SIMON**
Assistant Editor **ROXY POLK**
Designer **KAT LARSON**
Digital Art Technician **CHRISTINA McKENZIE**

Special thanks to **LEIGH BEACH, GARY CLAY,**
**SHANA DOERR, A.J. RATHBUN, KRISTEN STAR,**
**JEREMY VANHOOZER,** and everyone at PopCap Games.

Scholastic edition: December 2015
ISBN 978-1-50670-068-7

10 9 8 7 6 5 4 3 2 1
Printed in China

**DarkHorse.com | PopCap.com**

▷ No plants were harmed in the making of this comic. Numerous zombies
with various zombie-focused collegiate majors, however, definitely were.

This volume collects the stories found in *Plants vs. Zombies: Bully for You* #1–#3 and the *Plants vs. Zombies* "The Curse of the Flower-Bot" short story that appeared in *Free Comic Book Day 2015: All Ages*, originally published by Dark Horse Comics in 2015. | Published by Dark Horse Books, a division of Dark Horse Comics, Inc., 10956 SE Main Street, Milwaukie, OR 97222 | International Licensing: (503) 905-2377 | To find a comics shop in your area, call the Comic Shop Locator Service toll-free at 1-888-266-4226. | **PLANTS vs. ZOMBIES: BULLY FOR YOU.** Plants vs. Zombies © 2015 Electronic Arts Inc. Plants vs. Zombies and PopCap are trademarks of Electronic Arts Inc. All rights reserved. Dark Horse Books® and the Dark Horse logo are registered trademarks of Dark Horse Comics, Inc. All rights reserved. No portion of this publication may be reproduced or transmitted, in any form or by any means, without the express written permission of Dark Horse Comics, Inc. Names, characters, places, and incidents featured in this publication either are the product of the author's imagination or are used fictitiously. Any resemblance to actual persons (living or dead), events, institutions, or locales, without satiric intent, is coincidental.

NEIL HANKERSON Executive Vice President  TOM WEDDLE Chief Financial Officer  RANDY STRADLEY Vice President of Publishing  MICHAEL MARTENS Vice President of Book Trade Sales  SCOTT ALLIE Editor in Chief  MATT PARKINSON Vice President of Marketing  DAVID SCROGGY Vice President of Product Development  DALE LaFOUNTAIN Vice President of Information Technology  DARLENE VOGEL Senior Director of Print, Design, and Production  KEN LIZZI General Counsel  DAVEY ESTRADA Editorial Director  CHRIS WARNER Senior Books Editor  CARY GRAZZINI Director of Print and Development  LIA RIBACCHI Art Director  CARA NIECE Director of Scheduling  MARK BERNARDI Director of Digital Publishing

7

WAIT A SECOND-- I THINK I *REMEMBER* THAT FACE.

AND ALSO THAT *CRANIAL EXPANSE.* WASN'T THAT THE WEIRD GUY WHO...

"...USED TO STEAL CANDY FROM HIGH SCHOOLERS, BACK WHEN I HAD MY DELIVERY BIKE?"

HEY!

Bag 4 Stealin'

Candy for HIGH SCHOOLERS

STEALING CANDY FROM *HIGH SCHOOLERS* WAS BAD ENOUGH, BUT NOW ZOMBOSS IS EVEN *MEANER!*

I *WON'T* STAND FOR THIS!

THIS LEAVES ME... *NO CHOICE!*

Things to do Today

Standing for this?

NO CHOICE!

I HAVE TO MAKE A *MYSTERIOUS* CALL.

AAAH, YES. HERE WE ARE.

HERE! OUR NEW EVIL PLAN IS BORN! HERE, WE LAY THE FOUNDATIONS OF A PLAN SO SINISTER THAT THE SKIES THEMSELVES WILL SHED TEARS!

A PLAN SO DEVASTATING THAT THE VERY STREETS WILL SHAKE WITH THE TREAD OF TEN THOUSAND ZOMBIE FEET!

AND YET, EVEN THE THUNDER OF OUR FOOTFALLS WILL NOT DROWN AWAY THE CRIES OF HORROR WHEN WE—

THIS YOUR CAR, BUDDY?

YOU CAN'T DOUBLE-PARK HERE.

SOON...

CURSES! A NINETY-DOLLAR TICKET.

BUT...NO MATTER. SOON, MONEY WILL BE MEANINGLESS, BECAUSE ALL RICHES WILL BE MINE!

THIS CITY WILL BE MINE! THIS WORLD WILL BE MINE, AND THE SKIES WILL CRY HAVOC WHEN I UNLEASH THE DARK HORDES OF MY—

HEH HEH HEH! A DAY OF THEFTS. PETTY, BUT... SO SATISFYING.

IT REMINDS ME OF...

"...MY COLLEGE DAYS."

"LIKE WHEN I WAS STEALING MUMMIES FROM THE MUSEUM.."

HEH HEH HEH.

BRAINS?

"INTERACTING WITH MY FELLOW STUDENTS."

OUT OF MY WAY!

THUMP

302

"AND MY TEACHERS."

OUT OF MY WAY!

THUMP

"AND REVELING IN THE SIMPLE BEAUTY OF NATURE DURING OUR FIELD TRIPS."

OUT OF MY WAY!

THUMP

"YES, YOU SEE, NOTHING WAS GOING TO STAND IN MY WAY OF BECOMING THE YOUNGEST STUDENT EVER TO GAIN A DOCTORATE IN THANATOLOGY."

19

27

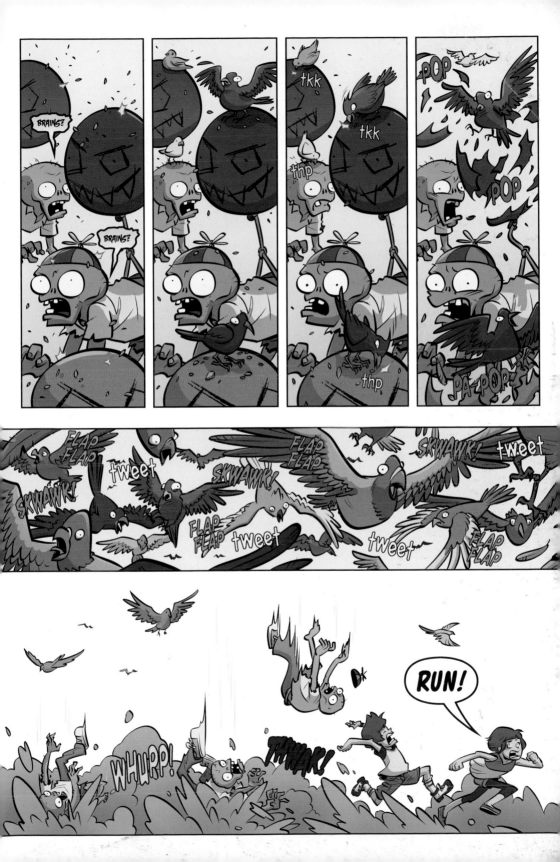

FLOPPA-FLOOP

...EANWHILE...

HE CAN'T DO IT! NO MAN ALIVE COULD EAT ALL THAT ICE CREAM BEFORE IT MELTS!

DON'T *LOOK,* KIDS! DON'T *LOOK!*

MOMMY, I'M SCARED!

AND ELSEWHERE...

WE NEED SOME MORE *TAPE* OVER HERE!

THE ZOMBIES ARE *EVERYWHERE!* HOW DID IT GET THIS BAD?

I'LL TELL YOU HOW. IT'S ALL BECAUSE OF...

34

44

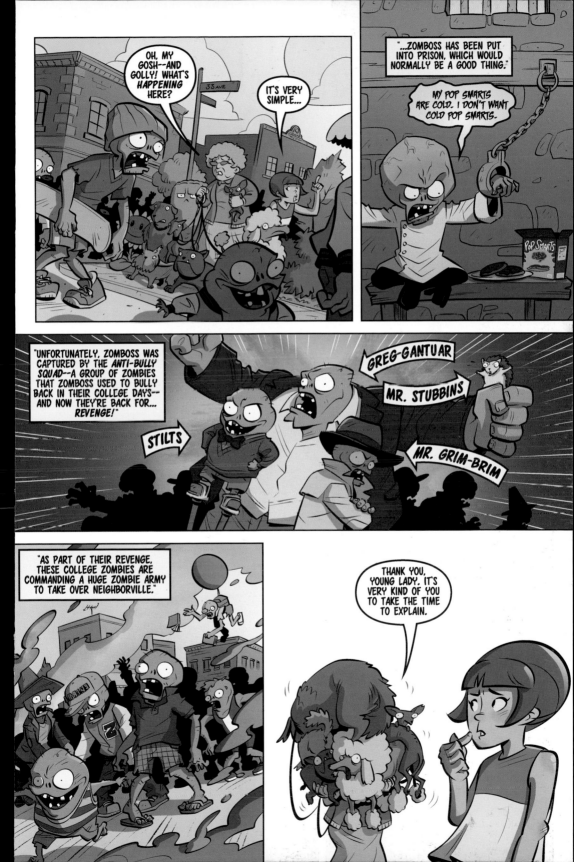

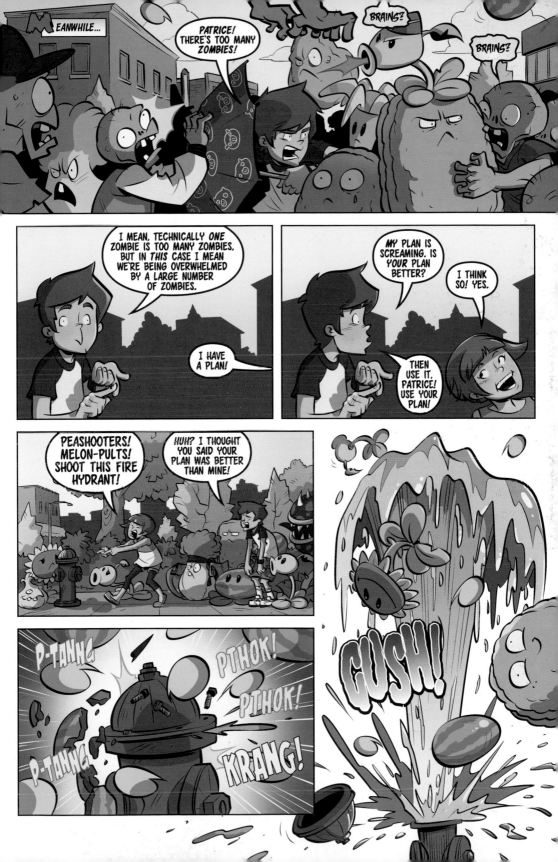

HMMM....THOSE FOOLS! THOSE FOOLISH FOOLS! THEY FORGOT TO SEARCH ME!

WHICH MEANS...

I STILL HAVE MY NEW ULTRA-TOASTY IMP-POWERED HEAT RAY!

THE ANTI-BULLY SQUAD THINKS THEY'VE REDUCED ME TO NOTHING--BUT WITH THIS HEAT RAY, IT IS CHILD'S PLAY TO ENACT A FABULOUS PLAN.

IT WILL TAKE ONLY MOMENTS TO USE MY HEAT RAY TO SOLVE THE MOST NEFARIOUS PROBLEM I'VE EVER FACED.

THESE COLD POP SMARTS.

VWRRRRRRRP

CHRRRRR

OH, I SUPPOSE I COULD DO THIS, TOO.

BWAAAH! HA HA HA!

DANG IT, MR. STUBBINS! NOW I HAVE TO GET OUT OF HERE BEFORE--

GRRK!

GRAB!

AND SO...

CAPTURED AGAIN?!?!?

ANTI-BULLY SQUAD CITYWIDE TAKEOVER HQ

but don't tell anyone, OK?

THAT'S RIGHT! AND THIS TIME, WE WON'T BE SO FOOLISH AS TO FORGET ABOUT SEARCHING YOU.

ALTHOUGH WE MIGHT BE FOOLISH IN OTHER WAYS.

DON'T TELL HIM THAT!

HM...SOME SORT OF DEVICE HERE.

ANYTHING ELSE?

SQUICK!

PUFF!

PUFF!

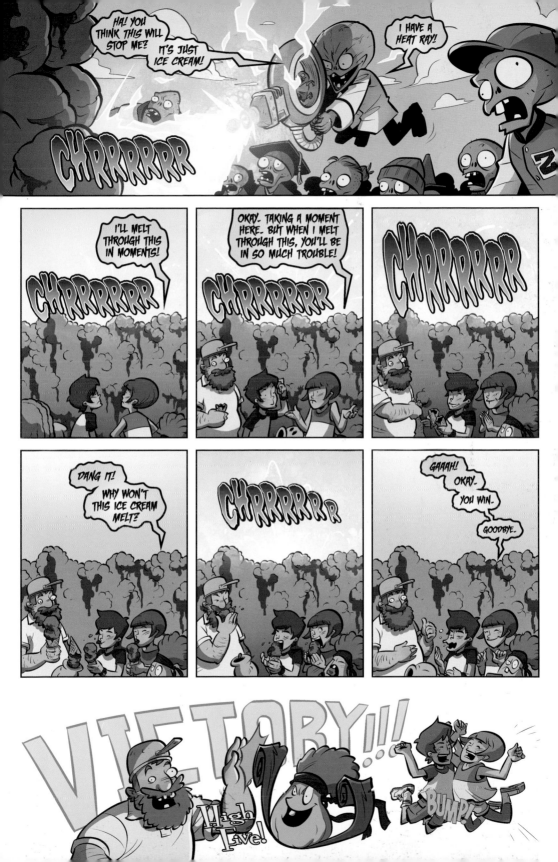

*Plants vs. Zombies* #1 Books-A-Million
variant cover by Colleen Coover

*Plants vs. Zombies* #3
cover by Ron Chan

# Plants vs. Zombies

## THE CURSE OF THE FLOWER-BOT

Written by **PAUL TOBIN**

Art by **RON CHAN**

Colors by **MATTHEW J. RAINWATER**

Letters by **STEVE DUTRO**

**FREE COMIC BOOK DAY**

The Free Comic Book Day story that introduced Tugboat, Frogpants, and Nigel Blimpbottom!

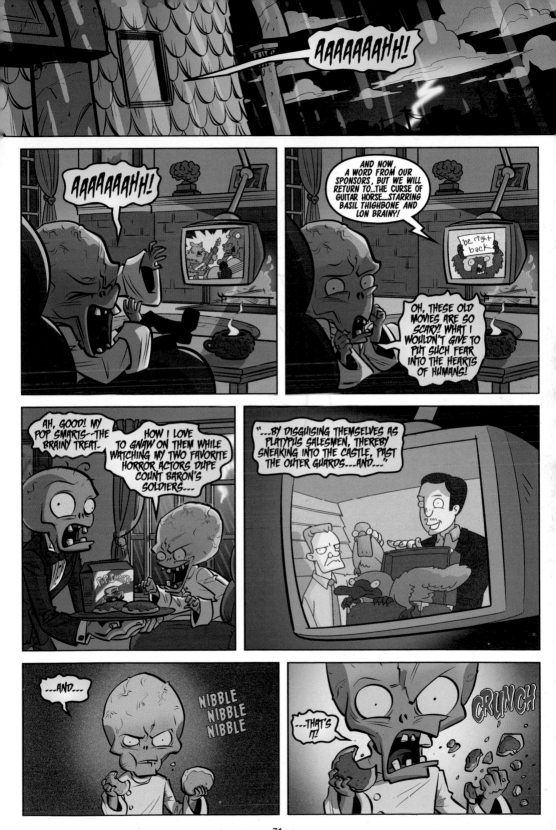

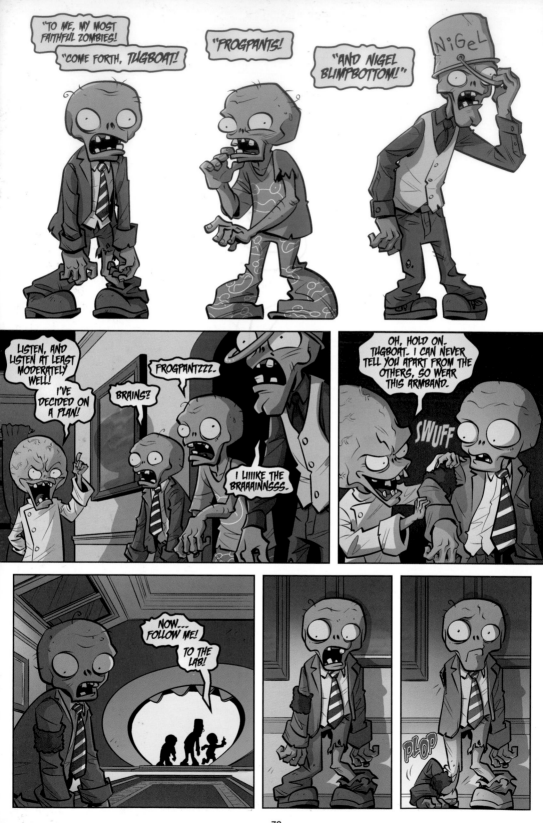

# BONUS STORIES

## POKEY PIQUENOSE

Written by PAUL TOBIN
Art by DUSTIN NGUYEN
Letters by STEVE DUTRO

## BONK CHOY BRO-DOWN!

Written by PAUL TOBIN
Art by DUSTIN NGUYEN
Letters by STEVE DUTRO

## BLOWN AWAY

Written by PAUL TOBIN
Art by JENNIFER L. MEYER
Letters by STEVE DUTRO

## THE SUNFROWNER

Written by PAUL TOBIN
Art by JENNIFER L. MEYER
Letters by STEVE DUTRO

## THE EMPTINESS

Written by PAUL TOBIN
Art and letters by PETER BAGGE

## MR. STUBBINS'S ADVENTURES

Written by PAUL TOBIN
Art and letters by PETER BAGGE

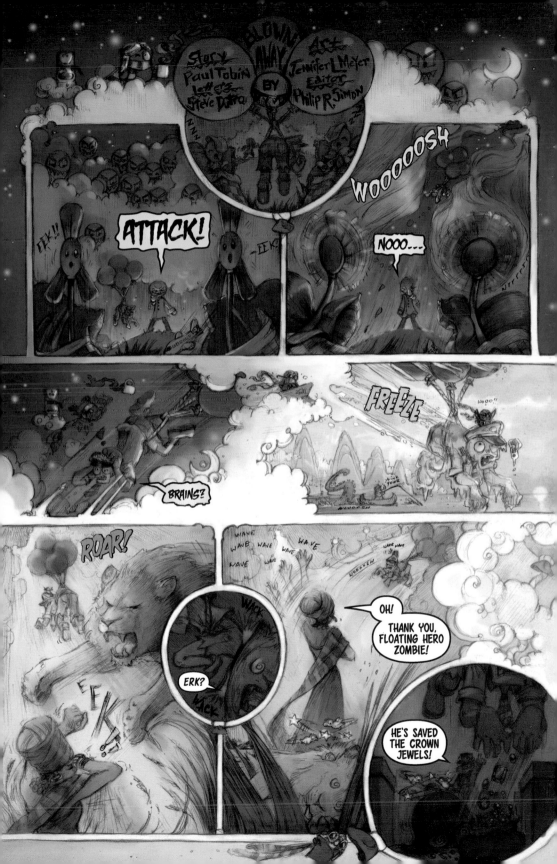

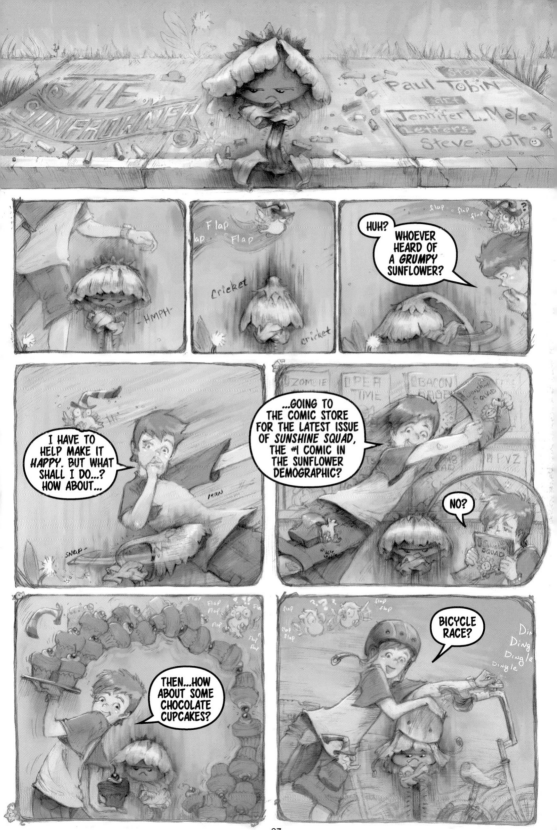

# CREATUR BIUS

Paul Tobin

Ron Chan

Matthew J. Rainwater

Steve Dutro

**PAUL TOBIN** is a critically acclaimed freckled person who has a detailed plan for any actual zombie invasion, based on creating a vast perfume and cologne empire—both of which would be vitally important in a zombie-infested world. Paul was once informed he "walks funny, like, seriously," but has recovered from this childhood trauma to write hundreds of comics for Marvel, DC, Dark Horse, and many others, including such creator-owned titles as *Colder* and *Bandette*, as well as *Prepare to Die!*—his debut novel. His *Genius Factor* series of novels about a fifth-grade genius and his war against the Red Death Tea Society begins in March of 2016 from Bloomsbury Publishing. Despite his many writing accomplishments, Paul's greatest claim to fame is his ability to win water levels in *Plants vs. Zombies* without using any water plants.

**RON CHAN** is a comic book and storyboard artist, video game fan, and occasional jujitsu practitioner. He was born and raised in Portland, Oregon, where he still lives and works as a member of the local artist collective Periscope Studio. His comics work has been published by Dark Horse, Marvel, and Image Comics, and his storyboarding work includes boards for 3-D animation, gaming, user-experience design,

and advertising for clients such as Microsoft, Amazon Kindle, Nike, and Sega. He really likes drawing Bonk Choys. (He also enjoys eating actual bok choy in real life.)

Residing in the cool, damp forests of Portland, Oregon, **MATTHEW J. RAINWATER** is a freelance illustrator whose work has been featured in advertising, web design, and independent video games. On top of this, he also self-publishes several comic books, including *Trailer Park Warlock*, *Garage Raja*, and *The Feeling Is Multiplied*—all of which can be found at MattJRainwater.com. His favorite zombie-bashing strategy utilizes a line of Bonk Choys with a Wall-nut front guard and Threepeater covering fire.

**STEVE DUTRO** is a comic book letterer from northern California who can also drive a tractor. He graduated from the Kubert School and has been in the comics industry for decades, working for Dark Horse (*The Fifth Beatle*, *The Evil Dead*, *Eden*), Viz, Marvel, and DC. Steve's last encounter with zombies was playing zombie paintball in a walnut orchard on Halloween. He tried to play the *Plants vs. Zombies* video game once but experienced a full-on panic attack and resolved to stick with calmer games . . . like *Gears of War*.

# MORE DARK HORSE ALL-AGES TITLES

## AW YEAH COMICS! AND . . . ACTION!

Cornelius and Alowicious are just your average comic book store employees, but when trouble strikes, they are . . . Action Cat and Adventure Bug! Join their epic all-ages adventures as they face off—with the help of Adorable Cat and Shelly Bug—against their archnemesis, Evil Cat, and his fiendish friends!

ISBN 978-1-61655-558-0 | $12.99

## USAGI YOJIMBO

In his latest adventure, the rabbit *ronin* Usagi finds himself caught between competing gang lords fighting for control of a town called Hell, confronting a *nukekubi*— a flying cannibal head—and crossing paths with the demon Jei!

*Volume 25: Fox Hunt*
ISBN 978-1-59582-726-5 | $16.99

*Volume 26: Traitors of the Earth* | $16.99
ISBN 978-1-59582-910-8

*Volume 27: A Town Called Hell* | $16.99
ISBN 978-1-59582-970-2

## AGE OF REPTILES OMNIBUS

When Ricardo Delgado first set his sights on creating comics, he crafted an epic tale about the most unlikely cast of characters: dinosaurs. Since that first Eisner-winning foray into the world of sequential art he has returned to his critically acclaimed *Age of Reptiles* again and again, each time crafting a captivating saga about his saurian subjects.

ISBN 978-1-59582-683-1 | $24.99

## ANGELIC LAYER BOOK 1

Junior-high student Misaki Suzuhara just arrived in Tokyo to live with her TV-star aunt and attend the prestigious Eriol Academy. But what excites Misaki most is Angelic Layer— an arena game where you control a miniature robot fighter with your mind! Can Misaki's enthusiasm and skill take her to the top of the arena?

ISBN 978-1-61655-021-9 | $19.99